STONE BEASTS

BY
RICHARD TAYLOR

ILLUSTRATED BY
SEB CAMAGAJEVAC

Titles in Full Flight Gripping Stories

Midsummer Mutants	David Orme
Beekeeper	Danny Pearson
Labyrinth	Melanie Joyce
The Incredible Save	Alison Hawes
Sci-Fi Spy Guy	Roger Hurn
Ghost Camp	Jillian Powell
Stone Beasts	Richard Taylor
Alien Speed Smash	Jonny Zucker
Jet Pack Power	Jonny Zucker
Hero: A War Dog's Tale	Jane A C West

Badger Publishing Limited
Oldmedow Road, Hardwick Industrial Estate,
King's Lynn PE30 4JJ
Telephone: 01438 791037

www.badgerlearning.co.uk

2 4 6 8 10 9 7 5 3 1

Stone Beasts ISBN 978 1 84926 269 9

First edition © 2010
This second edition © 2014

Text © Richard Taylor 2010
Complete work © Badger Publishing Limited 2010

Badger Publishing would like to thank Jonny Zucker
for his help in putting this series together.

Publisher: David Jamieson
Editor: Danny Pearson
Design: Fiona Grant
Illustration: Seb Camagajevac

STONE BEASTS

Contents

Badger
LEARNING

New words:

half	started
incredible	stared
shoulder	silent
incredibly	believe

Main characters:

Phil Lewis

Godfrey

CHAPTER I
My First Gargoyle

Have you ever heard of a gargoyle?

No? Well, a gargoyle is a small statue, made of stone. It looks like a little monster or a demon.

You can sometimes see gargoyles on the roofs of churches or other old, spooky buildings.

Next time you walk around an old city, look up. You may see one staring down at you.

They can look very frightening, with their tongues hanging out of their mouths and their beady little eyes.

The first time I saw one I felt like it was watching me. I felt like it was going to jump down from the rooftop and eat me.

But they are only statues, nothing to be scared of. They are not real. That's what my dad told me.

And that's what everyone thought.

Until I, Phil Lewis, loser with no friends, noticed that the gargoyles of London had started to move.

Chapter 2
The School Trip

I was on a school trip when I first
noticed that the gargoyles were moving.

It was the coldest day I'd ever known.

I was on a trip to the Houses of
Parliament.

Parliament is the place where the Prime Minister goes to talk about running the country.

It is one of the most famous buildings in London.

We were standing outside on the snowy pavement.

It was very early in the morning. There was no one else around but an old man feeding the birds.

My teacher, Mr Collins, was telling my class all about the Prime Minister.

"The Prime Minister is the most important man in England," he said, pointing at the buildings.

But I wasn't listening. I was staring at a gargoyle.

It was the ugliest gargoyle I'd ever seen in my life. It sat above the main door, the one that the Prime Minister uses.

I had the same feeling that I had the first time I ever saw a gargoyle. The feeling that I was being watched.

I remembered what my Dad had told me. It's not real. It's only a statue. And that was when I saw it. That was when I saw the gargoyle move.

A bird was sitting on the rooftop next to it, trying to keep warm.

Then it happened. As quick as a flash, the gargoyle's tongue popped out and grabbed the bird. It pulled it into its mouth.

My body felt as cold as the ice on the ground. I looked around me to see if anyone else had noticed, but all my class were listening to Mr Collins.

I told myself I had imagined it. But I couldn't stop thinking about what I had seen. The gargoyle had moved.

Mr Collins had finished his talk.

I started to walk back to the coach with my class. I told myself that my mind was tricking me.

Suddenly, I felt a bony hand on my shoulder, stopping me. Was it the gargoyle? I shut my eyes, ready for its bite.

I turned to see a pale, sickly face. It was the old man. The old man that had been feeding the birds.

CHAPTER 3
Secret Guards

"What did you see?" snapped the old man.

"Nothing," I lied.

"Rubbish. Tell me what you saw, boy."

He squeezed my shoulder. I looked to my class for help, but they had gone.

I was full of fear. His staring eyes reminded me of the gargoyle.

I told the old man the truth.
"I saw a gargoyle move," I said.

The old man's face changed. It became friendly. He let go of my shoulder.

"I knew it," he said to himself.

"Who are you?" I asked.

"My name is Godfrey," he said. "And I have been watching these statues every day for the last 50 years."

"Why?" I asked.

"Because they are alive."

My heart beat like a drum. "How do you know?" I asked.

"I know because I made them," he said.

CHAPTER 4
Godfrey's Story

Godfrey took me to a café and bought me a cup of tea.

"50 years ago," began Godfrey, "I worked for the Prime Minister. My job was to guard him. He is an important man and many people wanted him dead. I had to think of a way to protect him."

"What did you do?" I asked.

"Well, back when I was in the army I was very good at building things. So I built those gargoyles. They are the two best robots ever made."

"But they are also deadly. They can rip a man to bits in seconds."

"You built them to protect the Prime Minister?" I said.

"That's right. They would be his secret guards. But I built them too well. They were too clever. And they were evil. They became more than just robots. I heard them talking about how they were going to kill the Prime Minister. Rip him apart and take over the country. But when I tried to warn him, he thought I had gone mad. I lost my job. That's why I've been watching them for the last fifty years."

"Why didn't the gargoyles kill you?" I asked.

"Because I'm the only person they fear. I built them and I know their only weakness. But I am getting very old.

That's why the gargoyles have been waiting so long. They are waiting for me to become too weak to fight them. Now I am very ill. And as soon as the gargoyles find out, they will attack."

"We must tell the police," I said.

"Do you think they'd believe us?" said Godfrey. "They'd try to lock us up. Only we can stop those little monsters."

"How?" I asked. "I'm only a kid. I'm a loser."

"I need you," said Godfrey. "I am too old and slow. As I said, the gargoyles have a weakness. I built them like wind-up toys.

They have cogs inside them, like clocks.
They have a lever on their foot. If you
turn it the wrong way, the cogs inside
them will break. They will die."

"Just like if you wind a toy the wrong
way," I said.

"Yes," said Godfrey. "That's right. Now
– are you ready to risk your life to save
your country?"

CHAPTER 5
The Climb

I didn't have a choice. If I didn't try, the Prime Minister would be dead. Ripped apart by Godfrey's monsters.

So that's why nine hours later, I, Phil Lewis – school geek – was climbing the walls of the Houses of Parliament.

Trying to sneak up on two sleeping, killer gargoyles.

I was scared. More scared than I had ever been in my life.

Godfrey had told me the gargoyles slept for just ten minutes every day, just after midnight.

That would be my only chance to get near them. They needed to 'sleep' to keep working.

My head was spinning. The stone wall was like ice. I felt like my fingers could snap off with the cold. But I climbed on, higher and higher towards the stone beasts.

Suddenly, I froze. I nearly fell with fright.

I had grabbed the stone foot of one of the gargoyles. I could see the lever that I had to turn to destroy it. But if I had woken it up, the gargoyle could devour me, as quickly as it had eaten the bird.

I heard a noise like grinding teeth.

The gargoyle's head was starting to turn. I quickly reached for the lever. I couldn't quite get to it. The gargoyle was looking right at me now.

I stretched again and this time grabbed the lever.

The gargoyle's eyes shut and a deafening screech rang out.

The gargoyle fell from the rooftop,

almost taking me with it.

There was a mighty crash as it hit the ground. The gargoyle smashed like glass.

I had destroyed one. But was the other woken by the noise?

I pulled myself up onto the roof and there it was, standing in front of me.

Covered in snow, it stretched out its
wings. It looked like a monstrous eagle.
Its sharp teeth shone in the frost.

"You killed my brother," it screeched.
"I'm going to tear you apart."

I shut my eyes and fell to my knees. I had failed. I waited for the end.

Then I heard that horrible screeching noise again.

I looked up and saw the gargoyle starting to fall forward. I just managed to roll away before it crushed me.

Behind it was Godfrey. He had turned the gargoyle's lever and saved my life.

But he looked like he was going to
collapse with tiredness. Old and sick, he
must have climbed up after me.

I grabbed his head before it hit the roof.
He had used the last of his energy
stopping the monster he had built.

CHAPTER 6
A Hero's Grave

Godfrey was buried a week later.

He had no friends or family. I was the only one that visited his grave.

There were gargoyles on the church rooftop. But they sat silently, watching over the dead hero.

The Prime Minister's life had been saved but no one would ever know who to thank. He never even knew he was in danger.

I never got a medal either. Not even a thank you or my picture in the paper.

But I didn't care. From that day on, I stopped being a loser.

Because I had a secret. I had stopped the stone beasts.

GARGOYLES

The word for gargoyle means
waterspewer, or water spitter.
A building that has gargoyles on it is
said to be "gargoyled".

Gargoyles were originally placed on
buildings to divide the flow of rainwater
off the roof to stop the potential damage
from a rainstorm. A trough is cut in the
back of the gargoyle and rainwater flows
through the open mouth.

Later they were used more for decoration
and they were said to scare off any evil or
harmful spirits.

Gargoyles can appear in all shapes, from
monks to combinations of real animals
and people. Some gargoyles are meant to
look funny and some are meant to look
evil and scary.

Animal gargoyles

The Egyptians, Greeks, and Romans all used animal-shaped waterspouts. Below is a list of some animals commonly used as gargoyles, and some of the meanings behind them.

Eagle

A powerful bird that was said to be able to kill dragons. Eagles were respected for their ability to see far away objects.

Lion

Long ago, lions were linked to the Sun, most likely due to their golden manes. During the medieval period lions became the symbol of pride.

Dog

Dogs were the most common animal crafted as a gargoyle. Dogs were seen as faithful, loyal, and intelligent, making them excellent guards.

Wolf

Although the wolf was a feared creature in medieval times, it was also respected. Wolves have the ability to live well in a group (a pack). They were seen as good leaders.

Snake

The serpent represents a struggle between good and evil. They were thought to be able to live forever due to the shedding of their skin.

Monkey

Monkeys were seen as stupid and mischievous creatures.

31

QUESTIONS

- *Where are you likely to see a gargoyle?*

- *Where was Phil on his school trip?*

- *What did Phil see one of the gargoyles eat?*

- *Why had Godfrey invented the gargoyles in the first place?*

- *How long did the gargoyles sleep for every day?*

- *Are there any gargoyles in your local area?*

- *What animal gargoyle was said to be able to kill dragons?*

- *What animal gargoyle was said to be stupid and mischievous?*